The Bumblebear

Nadia Shireen

JONATHAN CAPE · LONDON

FOR NOAH, OF COURSE

JONATHAN CAPE

UK | USA | Canada | Ireland | Australia
India | New Zealand | South Africa
Jonathan Cape is part of the Penguin Random House
group of companies whose addresses can be found at
global.penguinrandomhouse.com.
www.penguin.co.uk
www.puffin.co.uk
www.ladybird.co.uk

Penguin
Random House
UK

First published 2016
This BookTrust edition published 2017
001

Printed in China

A CIP catalogue record for this book is
available from the British Library

ISBN: 978–1–780–08117–5

All correspondence to:
Jonathan Cape, Penguin Random House Children's,
80 Strand, London WC2R 0RL

MIX
Paper from
responsible sources
FSC
www.fsc.org   FSC® C018179

Once there was a bear
called Norman, who loved honey.
He really, **really**, **really** loved it.

And he was always sad when it ran out.

But getting hold
of more honey
was always
a bit . . .

. . . tricky.

"If only I could be a bee," he sighed,
"I could have as much honey as I liked."

And then Norman had a quite AMAZING and BRILLIANT idea.

It was an ordinary morning
at Bee School.

"Hello, bees!" said the Queen, who was in charge. "We have a NEW bee at Bee School today."

Oooooh!

said the little bees.

"Everyone, say hello to . . .

...Norman!"

"Hullo!"
said Norman.

O**ooo**h!

said the little bees.

"Aren't you a bit . . . big?" asked Amelia,
who was a rather *clever* little bee.

"Um, I'm a SPECIAL bee," said Norman. "I come
from a land far, far away called . . . GIANT BEE LAND."

"Hmmm . . ." said Amelia.

But then it was time for lessons to start.

BEE SCHOOL Daily Planner
Name: Norman

They began the day

with some painting.

Then Norman joined in

with buzzing practice . . .

BUZZ! BUZZ!

BUZZ! BUZZ! BUZZZ!

before everyone

settled down for a nap.

The bees showed him all sorts of games during playtime,

and Norman was brilliant at waggly dancing!

And then it was time to go home.

"Bee School is amazing!" thought Norman. He couldn't wait to come back the next day.

The next morning was **even** better!

Norman was very good at finding smelly flowers.

The bees really liked him.

He was so funny and friendly and he always tried his best . . .

. . . even during flying lessons.

After lunch, the bees learned how to chase away anyone who came after their honey, like spiders, mice, toads . . . or **bears**.

Amelia still felt there was something a bit *odd* about Norman. She tried to work out what it was . . .

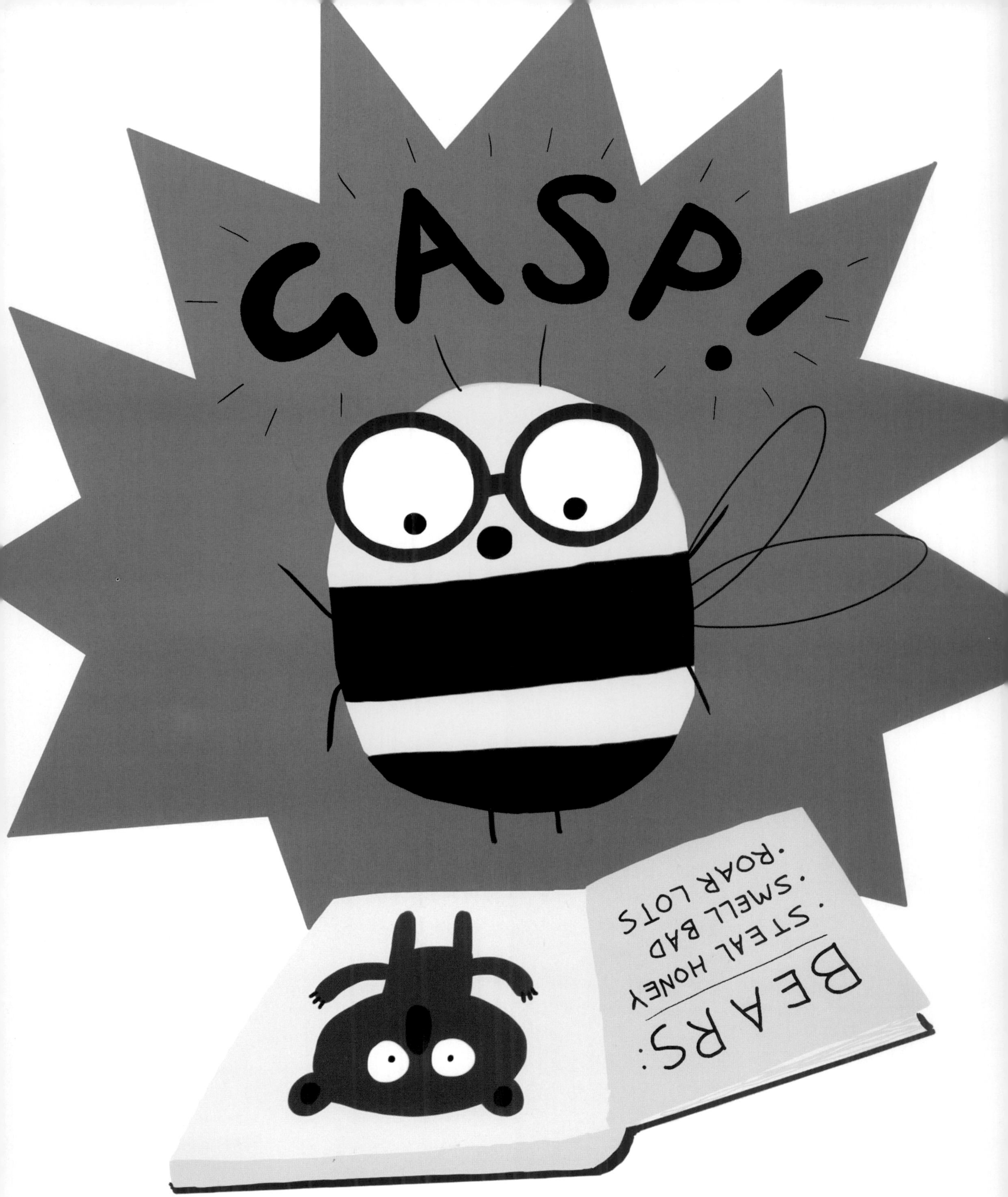
GASP!
BEARS:
· STEAL HONEY
· SMELL BAD
· ROAR LOTS

Amelia told the other bees what she had found out, but they didn't believe her.

"Of course Norman's a bee!" they said. "Just look at him!"

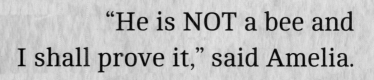

"He is NOT a bee and I shall prove it," said Amelia.

After all,
he really, really, really
loved honey.

"See, Norman isn't a bee –
he's a BEAR!" said Amelia.

"What the jiggins?" gasped all the little bees.

"Mmph?" said Norman.

He was asked to leave
Bee School **at once**.

With Norman gone,
things were very quiet
at Bee School.

"Norman was such a
funny bee," sighed the bees.

"Norman was such a
busy bee," sighed Amelia.

"Norman was a **naughty bear**,"
said the Queen, "and Bee School
is no place for bears!"

But later that night, the bees
heard a loud . . .

CRASH!

and a diabolical

ROWR!

"Oh no!"

they cried.

"IT'S A BEAR!"

And this bear was BIG and NASTY, and trampled all over Bee School. It grabbed the hive and started to SHAKE IT!

The bees tumbled out in a panic!

They tried to chase
the bear away
but it was just
too big and
too bad.

BUT
THEN . . .

The bees were saved and Norman was a

HERO!

HONEY

They gave him a big pot of honey, and
the Queen presented him with a special award.

"You definitely aren't a bee," said the Queen.
"But you are no ordinary bear. You are, I think –
a BUMBLEBEAR."

And bumblebears were definitely allowed to go back to

BEE SCHOOL!

THE END

Contents

Words in bold, **like this**, are explained in the Glossary.

Introducing the Indus River

A great river

The Indus is one of the world's greatest rivers. It stretches for a total distance of around 2900 kilometres (1800 miles) and carries twice as much water per year as the Nile, the world's longest river. But it is not just its geography that makes it a great river. For thousands of years the Indus River has been important to the people living in the surrounding lands. **Archaeologists** working in the Indus region have discovered the remains of ancient **settlements**. These show that the Indus was once home to a great **civilization**, which is known as the Indus valley civilization or sometimes as the Harappan civilization after Harappa, one of the first settlements to be found. Archaeologists are still investigating the Indus valley civilization, but we know that it is over 5000 years old and that the key to its success was the Indus River.

The Indus is still very important to the people living alongside it today. This is particularly true for the people of Pakistan, as the Indus flows through their country for most of its length. Because of this, many of Pakistan's most important settlements are located along its banks. The Pakistani population of around 150 million people are almost completely dependent on the Indus, which provides them with water for farming, for industry and for drinking.

River glossary

Confluence – *the point where two rivers join.*

Delta – *where the river joins the sea.*

Mouth – *the ending point of a river.*

Reaches – *used to describe sections of the river (upper, middle and lower reaches).*

River course – *the path followed by a river from source to mouth.*

Source – *the starting point of a river.*

Tributary – *a river or stream that joins another (normally bigger) river.*

From source to mouth

The source of the Indus River is high on the Tibetan **plateau** in China. There, at an **altitude** of over 5000 metres, the Indus emerges from Manasarovar Lake. This is the start of its 2900 kilometre (1800 mile) journey to the Arabian Sea. In its upper **reaches** the young Indus is fed by **melt-waters** from the snowfields and glaciers of the Himalayas (the highest mountain range in the world) which it passes as it heads north-west into India. The Indus then continues through the mountains of northern India. As it crosses into northern Pakistan it collects yet more melt-water from the Karakoram and Hindu Kush mountain ranges.

Swollen by all the melt-water, the narrow Indus is now a raging torrent. As it roars through the mountains it carves some of the world's deepest **gorges**. The people of this region know the Indus as 'Lion River'. Legend has it that the Indus was born from the mouth of a lion and that whoever drinks from it will become heroic like a lion!

The Indus cuts narrow gorges through the mountains as it rushes to the sea.

The Indus has the seventh largest delta in the world. It is one and a half times the size of Israel and almost three times the size of Jamaica!

This is a satellite image of the Indus delta, which covers c30,000 square kilometres (12,000 square miles).

Just to the east of Gilgit in northern Pakistan the Indus turns and heads south-west for the remainder of its journey. At Kalabagh in northern Pakistan, the Indus breaks free from the narrow mountain gorges. Within 2 kilometres (1 mile) it slows down dramatically and spreads out to around 4 kilometres (about 2 miles) in width. The Indus then flows gently through the dry **plains** of central and southern Pakistan. It is here that the Indus is a vital source of water for local people. In this part of its journey the Indus is joined by five **tributaries** – the Jhelum, Chenab, Ravi, Beas, and Sutlej rivers. These rivers give the region Punjab, meaning 'land of five rivers', its name. As it nears the Arabian Sea the Indus spreads out to form 'the mouths of the Indus'. This is a giant **delta** that is some 240 kilometres (150 miles) wide where it meets the sea.

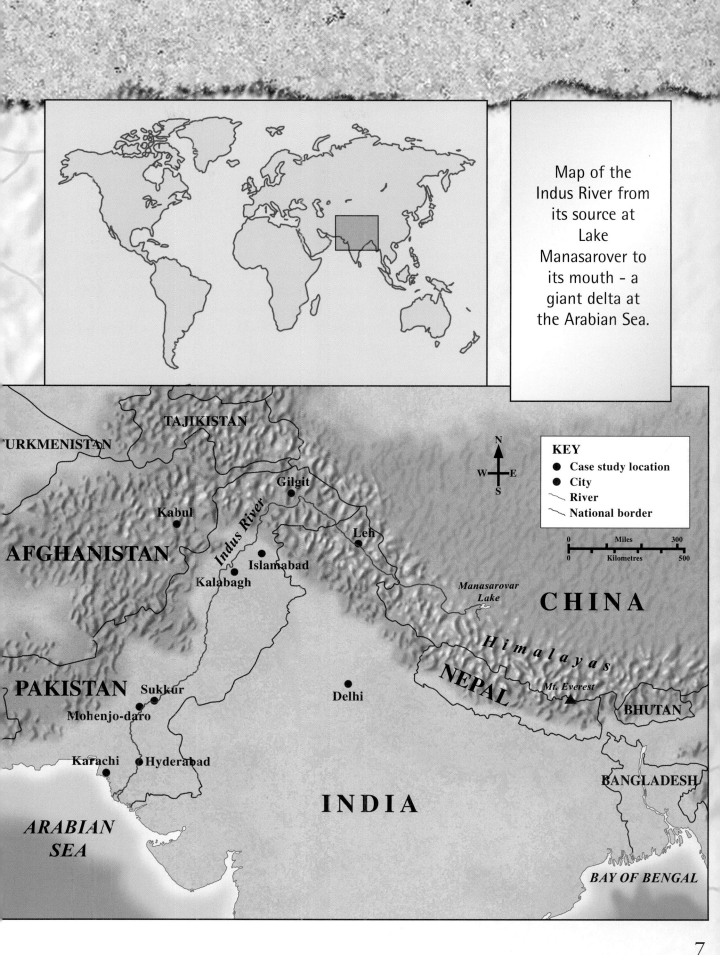

Map of the Indus River from its source at Lake Manasarover to its mouth - a giant delta at the Arabian Sea.

KEY
- ● Case study location
- ● City
- — River
- ⌇ National border

Settlements of the Indus

Settlements along the Indus vary depending on the type of land the river flows through. Mountainous areas have little level ground to build on, and have severe snow and ice for much of the year, cutting them off from the rest of the world. Despite these difficulties, there are a few key settlements here, such as Leh in northern India. These settlements have developed because of their location on historic trade routes (see map on page 22). Merchants used these routes to transport goods between markets that were sometimes hundreds of miles apart. The upper Indus is on the trade route between China to the East, and between Europe and the Middle East to the West.

Most of the Indus' settlements are along its middle and lower reaches. Here there is plenty of level land for building on. The annual flooding of the Indus River has also created a valley rich in **nutrients**. These are carried down in the **sediment** from the mountains. The nutrient-rich soil is ideal for farming and has supported **agriculture** for thousands of years. Some villages along the Indus became busy markets, which people travelled to from great distances. Over time they became important river settlements. Some of them have populations of over a million people today!

People settled in small villages along the Indus, living and farming in a similar way to the people who live there today.

The sprawling city of Hyderabad shows how rapidly some of the settlements along the Indus have grown.

In this book we will explore some of the Indus' best-known settlements. We will follow a passage through time, starting with the ancient city of Mohenjo-daro and ending with the relatively modern city of Karachi, which is now one of the largest cities in the world. We will look at why those settlements formed where they did and how they have changed over time. What are they like today and how might they change in the future? Most importantly of course we will discover how the settlements are linked to the Indus. By looking at the settlements of the Indus and the people living there we can see how the importance of the region and the river has changed over time.

What's in a name?

The origins of local names show the close ties between the Indus and the lands and people surrounding it. The country name India comes from Indus. Early records show that the Indus was originally known by its Sanskrit name 'Sindhu'. Over time this changed under the influence of different languages, especially Arabic. Arabians pronounced 's' as 'h' and so called the river and its people 'Hindus'. 'Hinduism', the name for the dominant religion in India, came from this. The river became known as the Indus, and India was used to describe the lands to the east of the Indus.

Mohenjo-daro: city from the past

Ancient secrets

Archaeologists have found the remains of about 1500 ancient **settlements** in the Indus valley. This evidence shows that many settlements were small farming or fishing villages, but some were larger, sophisticated cities. The largest of these cities was Mohenjo-daro. At the height of its development it may have had a population of up to 40,000 people.

The ruins of Mohenjo-daro, from 2600 to 2500 BC, were discovered in 1922 and are still being **excavated** today. While many of the excavated items provide us with a glimpse of what city-life might have been like almost 5000 years ago, some remain shrouded in mystery. For example, their writing, similar to Egyptian hieroglyphics, is still not properly understood.

A gift of the Indus

Mohenjo-daro was very dependent on the Indus River. The annual flooding of the river created fertile **plains** in which it was possible to grow wheat, barley, millet, fruit and vegetables easily. The soil was so good that it produced a regular surplus of food. This meant that people could do work other than farming. They could then trade their skills with the farmers in return for food.

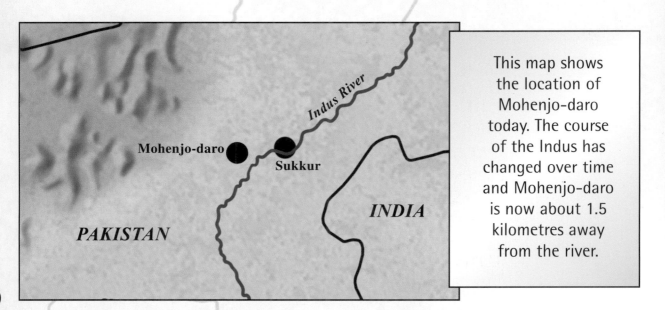

This map shows the location of Mohenjo-daro today. The course of the Indus has changed over time and Mohenjo-daro is now about 1.5 kilometres away from the river.

Over time, some people developed into highly skilled craftsmen, making pottery, cloth, jewellery and leather goods. Others began to trade these goods with people from as far afield as Mesopotamia (modern-day Syria and Iraq) and Egypt. The Indus provided a vital transport route for its trade to the Arabian coast and beyond.

Pictures found at Mohenjo-daro show us that goods such as grain, timber and cotton were transported using a form of flat-bottomed boat. Similar boats are still used on the Indus today. The Indus also provided the people of Mohenjo-daro with fish to eat. Fragments of pottery that have been unearthed in the city clearly show images of nets, hooks and different types of fish, some of which are still found in the river today.

Flat-bottomed boats can get closer to the land, for loading, than other boats. They are still used on the Indus today, to transport grain and other goods.

FACT

Mohenjo-daro means 'mound of the dead' in English. It was called this because local people believed it was an ancient burial place. They may have been mistaken, however, as very few bodies have ever been found.

A planned city

Archaeologists have discovered that Mohenjo-daro was a very organized city. The whole city, from houses to neighbourhoods and street networks, was carefully planned.

The city had two main parts: the **citadel** and the lower city. The citadel stands on a man-made earthen mound, 12 metres above the surrounding flood plain. This provided protection from the regular flooding of the Indus. The citadel was well placed for watching the city and river below. This may have helped the religious and political leaders, who probably lived there, to stay in power.

Water was very important in the city. The 'Great Bath' is the most famous feature of the citadel. It could be the world's first-ever swimming pool! More likely is that it was used for **ritual** bathing by people praying for a good harvest or for safety during the floods. The remains of what may be a granary also exist. Grain was essential food for the city, and the river provided the fertile land and means of transporting it, proving just how vital the Indus was for the city.

This plan of Mohenjo-daro shows how well organized and how large the settlement was.

The lower city makes up most of Mohenjo-daro. It is neatly organized around a grid-pattern street network, similar to that of most US cities. The main streets are up to 9 metres wide. They would once have been bustling with people and carts, carrying goods to and from the river. Narrower alleyways were built at right angles to the main streets. Doorways to the houses were located here, away from the dust and noise of the main street.

Archaeologists have only excavated a third of the lower city, but they believe it is divided into neighbourhoods. There is a wealthy neighbourhood where the houses are much larger. There is also an area where they think many of the skilled craftworkers lived.

Amazingly, Mohenjo-daro's houses enjoyed features that some settlements around the world still

FACT

The clay bricks that were used to make Mohenjo-daro are all exactly 28cm x 14cm x 7cm. We know that children helped to make these bricks because of the small footprints found in them.

lack today. Many had their own private water supplies, with wells inside the houses. Bathrooms were also common, with paved-brick floors. Waste water was taken away in a city-wide system of covered drains. These were frequently inspected and cleaned or repaired. Several houses had toilets that were separately emptied and there were even neighbourhood rubbish bins to help keep the streets clean.

A city in decline

For about 800 years Mohenjo-daro was a thriving city, but around 1800 BC it fell into decline and was soon abandoned. No one knows why this happened. The discovery of skeletons at the site has led some to believe that invaders stormed the city and killed many of the people. The city may have declined following a change in the course of the Indus caused by an earthquake. Today the Indus is about 1.5 kilometres (almost a mile) to the east of Mohenjo-daro, but it used to flow just west of the city. Other rivers in the area dried up at this time, and the region is much drier than it used to be. This would have changed the pattern of flooding, severely affecting farming and trade along the Indus.

From the past to the present

Despite the city's decline, there are obvious links between the city of 5000 years ago and life along the Indus today. The design of some boats has changed little, and bullock carts used by riverside farmers today are almost identical to children's toys discovered at the ancient city.

The ruins at Mohenjo-daro attract many tourists every year.

c.3300 BC	c.2600 BC	c.2600 – 1800 BC	c.1800 BC
Small villages are established in the area around Mohenjo-daro.	Building of a planned city is begun at Mohenjo-daro.	Mohenjo-daro is a thriving trade city.	Mohenjo-daro falls into decline and is later abandoned.

Silt in the Indus can raise the water table and make flooding worse. Farmers haul the silt for the government and are able to keep it to use on their farms.

Boats even carry similar cargo, such as pottery and crops. Many of the skilled crafts that made Mohenjo-daro so impressive are still practised in Pakistan and India. They include beadwork, pottery, jewellery-making, tilework and weaving. In these ways, the Indus valley civilization survives in the lives of the people living there today.

Saving Mohenjo-daro

*Modern farming activities now threaten the ruins of Mohenjo-daro. **Irrigation** using water from the Indus has raised the **water table** under the city. As the water nears the surface it brings salts with it. These slowly disintegrate the clay bricks of Mohenjo-daro.*

Since 1972 the Pakistani government has been working with the international community to try and prevent such damage. A number of wells now pump water away from the foundations of the city. Farming in the area has been banned and attempts are being made to divert the waters of the Indus to reduce the risk of flooding.

But parts of the city have already begun to disintegrate. These are now being capped with mud to prevent them crumbling further. So, the ancient city of Mohenjo-daro is still locked in a battle with the Indus. The river that created the city may also be responsible for its destruction.

AD 1922	1948	1973	1980
Mohenjo-daro's ruins are discovered.	First attempts to conserve Mohenjo-daro are made.	Plans are approved to preserve Mohenjo-daro.	Mohenjo-daro becomes a World Heritage Site.

Sukkur: the great barrage

Shifting waters

For centuries, people living along the Indus have relied on its waters. However, sometimes the river has brought them great hardships. Some hardships have been short-lived, such as floods submerging parts of local villages and towns. Occasionally, though, the Indus undergoes major changes, seriously disrupting the lives of people living along it. One such change happened around 962 AD, when an earthquake caused the Indus to shift to its present-day channel. **Settlements** that once thrived on the banks of the Indus were stranded, sometimes several kilometres from the river. This happened to the ancient city of Aror, the ruins of which now lie 8 kilometres (5 miles) to the east of the Indus.

The people of Aror relocated and established a settlement alongside the new course of the Indus. This new settlement became the modern-day city of Sukkur. By the 13th century, Sukkur along with Rohri (on the opposite bank of the Indus) had a bustling port and was a centre for trading local agricultural produce. Sukkur's vegetable market remains one of the city's most lively attractions.

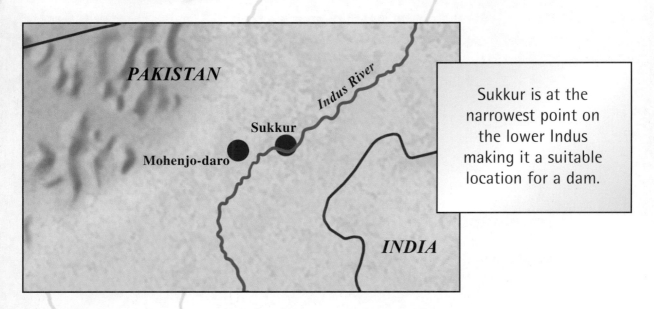

PAKISTAN

Indus River

Sukkur

Mohenjo-daro

INDIA

Sukkur is at the narrowest point on the lower Indus making it a suitable location for a dam.

Taming the Indus

Farmers in the Indus valley have always relied on the annual flooding of the river to provide the land with **nutrients** and water. Large parts of the valley receive very little rainfall and without the waters of the Indus it would not be possible to grow crops. The problem with natural flooding is that it can be very unreliable. Sometimes the floods bring too much water and sometimes they do not bring enough. Trying to predict when the floods will arrive is also a problem. Food production along the Indus valley has therefore been unstable.

In the 1840s the British took control of the area around Sukkur (known as Sindh) as part of the **British Empire**. They realized that if they could

control the waters of the Indus then more food could be grown. By 1847 they had devised a plan to tame the river by building a **barrage** across it. The barrage would allow the waters of the Indus to be stored and released slowly to water the fields of Sindh throughout the year.

Sukkur was chosen as the site for this barrage. As the narrowest point in the lower Indus, it was an obvious location to try to dam the river. Although planned, the British did not begin building the Sukkur barrage until 1923 and it took almost ten years to build. When it was finished in 1932 the flow of the Indus was controlled for the first time.

At 1418 metres in length, the Sukkur barrage is one of the largest dams in the world.

A giant water spider

The Sukkur barrage was built to divert the waters of the
Indus to **irrigate** (water) **uncultivated** land around Sukkur.
Irrigation is widely used in areas of low rainfall. Seven canals
were built to carry water from Sukkur to new areas of land.
Four canals stretch out to the west and three to the east.
From above they look like a giant seven-legged spider, with
each canal like a leg creeping out into the land beyond.
When it was built the Sukkur irrigation system was the
greatest in the world.

Irrigation canals, like this one, carry water from
the Sukkur barrage to the surrounding area.

It remains one of the world's largest systems today, with around 75,000 kilometres (47,000 miles) of canals irrigating close to 3 million hectares of land.

Crops on the irrigated land are grown to meet local needs and to sell (cash crops). Local crops include a wide variety of vegetables and different fruits. The area is particularly well known for its good bananas. The main cash crops include cotton, rice, sugar cane and wheat.

A commercial centre

Sukkur is today a major commercial centre for the trading and processing of **agricultural** produce. For example, raw cotton is taken to Sukkur for processing into thread. This is then used in local textile factories to make cloth and clothing. Other industries process different crops grown in the area. These include flour and rice **milling** and the manufacture of sweets from sugar cane. Sukkur is particularly well suited as a commercial centre because it has good road and rail connections, allowing trade with other parts of Pakistan and neighbouring Afghanistan. The road and rail bridges that cross the Indus in Sukkur are among the most important trade routes in Pakistan. The bridges can

span the river here because the distance is made shorter by Bukkur Island, which rests in the middle of the river.

The good transport connections and water supply have attracted new industries to set up in Sukkur, such as **tanneries**, metalworking and the manufacture of cement and chemicals. The river also continues to play a role in transporting raw materials and finished goods between Sukkur and settlements lower down the Indus, though it is less vital today. As Sukkur's commercial importance has grown, so too has its population. At the time the barrage was completed there were fewer than 60,000 people living in Sukkur, but by 2000 the city was home to 330,000 people – more than five times as many!

FACT

The Indus River system provides water that irrigates between 80–90 per cent of Pakistan's farmland. The remaining farmland relies on rainfall.

An uncertain future

The Sukkur barrage was the first to be built across the Indus, but there are now several others. Most are located upstream of Sukkur, on the Indus or one of its **tributaries**. Taking water from these barrages to irrigate crops has reduced the amount of water reaching Sukkur. This has caused major problems for Sukkur's irrigation system. More recently, some of the canals have had to be closed. Others have only been able to provide half the normal amount of water. The water shortage is also affecting Sukkur's agricultural economy. If it continues it could lead to job losses and force people to leave the city to work elsewhere. The problem is partly caused by poorly maintained canals. Leakages mean that up to 70 per cent of the water is lost, never even reaching the fields. If improved and maintained, the canals would allow water to be used more efficiently. Changes are needed if Sukkur is to continue to thrive in the future.

The Lansdowne Bridge, built over the Indus at Sukkur in 1888, allowed trains to travel from Karachi to the north more easily.

AD962	c.1250	c.1842	1847
Sukkur is founded.	Sukkur is established as a busy port.	British gain control of Sukkur.	First plans are made for a barrage at Sukkur.

The Mohana boat people

The Mohanas are a group of people who live on boats along the Indus and on nearby Manchar Lake. The Mohanas are thought to have lived like this for thousands of years and may date back to the time of Mohenjo-daro. They live in village groups of five to ten boats. Each boat (called a 'teen') is divided into separate living areas, and houses a family of six to ten people.

The Mohanas use reeds and other plants such as the lotus flower for food and to make goods such as woven reed mats. The Mohanas fish and also hunt waterfowl, but in a rather unusual way! They wade into the water with a stuffed egret (a bird similar to a heron) on their heads to trick the other birds. This allows them to get close enough to grab them.

Today the Mohanas are mainly found on Manchar Lake, despite government efforts since the 1970s to settle them along the Indus. Their livelihood is now threatened by pollution in the waters of the Indus and Manchar Lake. Fish catches have fallen dramatically and fewer birds are found in the area. More recently the Mohanas' unique way of life has begun attracting tourists.

1888	1923	1932
Lansdowne Rail Bridge is built across Indus at Sukkur.	Construction of Sukkur barrage begins.	Sukkur barrage is opened.

Leh: mountains and monasteries

Highland trading

Leh is the capital of the Ladakh region of northern India. Rock carvings in the region show that it has been inhabited for thousands of years. Early inhabitants would have been nomadic tribespeople. Nomads live on the move, travelling through their region in search of fresh grass for their animals, in this case, goats, sheep and yaks. Some people still live this way today.

FACT

Ladakh translated into English means 'many passes' – a reference to the numerous paths that cover this rugged mountain region.

The first permanent **settlements** in the area developed as centres of trade connected to the famous Silk Road. This was an overland trade route that connected China with the Middle East and Mediterranean Europe. It is thought to have first developed around the 6th century BC and was the major trade route across Asia for some 1500 years. The Indus and its **tributaries** created a path through the mountains and, as one of the few accessible routes in the landscape, it introduced new peoples to the upper Indus.

This map shows the borders and country names when the Silk Road trade route was at its height. Leh developed as a settlement because of the trade route.

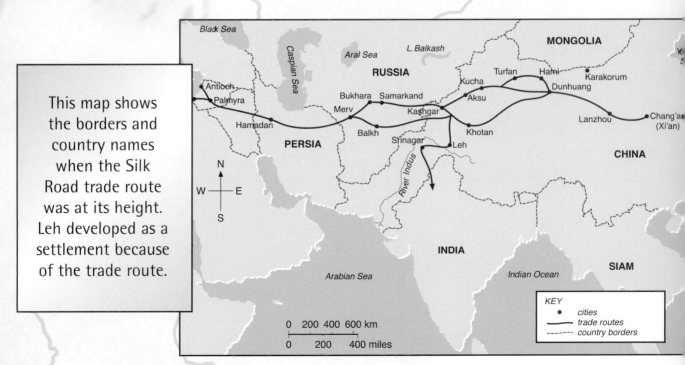

Terraced fields have been built into the mountainous terrain of the upper Indus.

Around 900 AD the Thi dynasty took control of the region. It was the first dynasty to develop here and ruled much of the Ladakh region from a capital built at Shey, on the banks of the Indus. **Buddhism** spread into the region from neighbouring Tibet. Over a hundred Buddhist monasteries, known as 'gompas', were built, many of which were located on the flatter land along the Indus. Leh, the current capital of Ladakh, was founded during the 16th century by Soyang Namgyal, a great leader who is famous for uniting the people of Ladakh into a single kingdom. He moved the capital from Shey to Leh, as it was closer to the Silk Road, the main trade route into China.

A hostile environment

The Ladakh region is a very hostile environment yet settlements do exist there. The area receives little rainfall and becomes bitterly cold in the long winters, with temperatures of -30°C or lower. Between November and April much of the region is completely cut off because of snow and ice. The areas of level land along the Indus and its tributaries provide one of the few places where people can settle, grow crops and build houses. The people living here have also learned how to tap the **melt-water** that flows from the surrounding mountains to the Indus. Small streams criss-cross the town of Leh carrying this precious water to the fields and houses.

Treasured kingdom

Leh is located just off the main Indus valley, on a **plateau** watered by melting glaciers in the Himalayas. This allows enough wheat, barley, peas and various vegetables to be grown, to feed the local population. Benefiting from its position on the trade route between India and China, Leh's status as a mountain **trading post** helped it develop. Merchants from Tibet, India, Pakistan and China would stop in Leh to trade in tea, salt, spices, semi-precious stones and household goods. One of Leh's most valued goods was cashmere. Cashmere wool is world-famous for its softness and warmth. It comes from the fleece of Himalayan goats reared in the mountains around Leh.

Leh's importance in the world of trade meant that several invading armies tried to capture it over the years. In 1834 general Zorawar Singh captured Leh for the Maharajah (prince) of Kashmir, to gain control of the city's valuable cashmere trade. Leh's king fled and built a new palace at Stok, about 10 kilometres (6 miles) south of Leh. In the mid-1840s, Leh became part of the British Empire. It remained under British control before becoming part of independent India in 1947.

The palace of Leh, damaged during the invasion of Zorawar Singh in 1834, can still be seen today.

From trade to tourism

In 1950, disputes between India and China led to the closure of the Chinese border and the end of Leh as a major trade centre. Many of Leh's residents found new jobs as labourers on government road-building schemes. The roads followed the course cut out by the Indus, and linked Leh to settlements in the rest of India.

Leh had a lot to offer to India's growing tourist industry. The new roads meant people could reach Leh fairly easily, although they could still be blocked by snow and ice for half of the year. Despite this, Ladakh was officially opened for tourism in 1974 and within a few years Leh had become a major tourist destination in northern India.

The fast-flowing waters of the upper Indus offer some of the world's best white water rafting. Many tourists use Leh as a base for rafting expeditions.

Leh's main attractions are its Buddhist history and its beautiful river and mountain scenery. Many tourists are interested in the gompas, the Buddhist monasteries that line the Indus and its tributaries, or come simply to enjoy the mountain environment, and can trek along the Indus paths, just as merchants would have done in the past. More recently the Indus has become popular for white water rafting. This allows tourists to see the river up close, and to pit their wits against its swirling and crashing waters.

25

Impact of tourism

The number of tourists visiting Leh has increased
steadily since 1974. Jobs and money from the tourist
industry attracted local people to move to the city,
causing a dramatic population increase. Between
1975 and 2000 Leh's population more than doubled
to around 27,500 people. Leh has grown to meet the
demands of tourism. An airport, built to make it easier for
people to reach Leh, has increased tourist numbers even more.
In 1998–99 Leh airport handled some 90,000 passengers, several
times more than the number of people that live in the city itself.

Hotels and guesthouses were opened in Leh to accommodate
tourists. Other services such as restaurants and gift shops have
also grown. Many of these are run by non-Ladakhi people from
Kashmir. Leh's tourist activities are placing enormous pressure

Most tourists arrive
in Leh by plane,
but some come
by car along
the roads that
follow the course
of the Indus.

900	c.1550	1834
First settlements are established in the area around Leh.	Leh is founded as the new capital by Soyang Namgyal.	Zorawar Singh captures Leh for the Maharaja of Kashmir.

The gompas of Ladakh

Dotted along the upper **reaches** *of the Indus as it passes through Ladakh are several Buddhist monasteries known as 'gompas'. Normally built on high ground, overlooking the river valleys below, the gompas have been places of worship for hundreds of years and are still in use today. Many contain historical Buddhist artworks such as face masks, religious costumes, and painted or embroidered scrolls known as 'thangkas'. Several of the gompas hold annual festivals to celebrate different aspects of the Buddhist faith, which attract people together from settlements across the region.*

on its environment. Mountain streams supplying water to Leh's agricultural fields have been running low because water is drawn off for tourists in the hotels and guesthouses. Some of this water is used for western-style flush toilets. These have caused an additional problem of leaking sewage that pollutes local streams and rivers like the Indus. Traditionally, people in Leh use compost toilets, which don't pollute or use any of the valuable water. Waste disposal has also polluted some local water supplies. To tackle these problems the Ladakh Ecological Development Group was established in 1984. They encourage local people and tourists to think more carefully about Leh's fragile mountain environment. They want people to enjoy Leh's historic sites and the Indus valley, but also to preserve them for future generations.

1840s	1974	1984
Leh becomes part of British-controlled India.	Leh is opened to international tourism.	Ladakh Ecological Development Group is established to protect Leh.

Hyderabad: the crossroads

An ideal location

Hyderabad is located on a hill on the east bank of the Indus. This is an ideal location for a **settlement**. The river provides any settlers with a regular water supply and is a natural route for transportation to neighbouring settlements. Hyderabad's hill-top location also acts as a lookout over the surrounding **plains** and provides safety and protection from any invading forces. The benefits of Hyderabad's location have long been recognized. Its ancient name, Nerun Kot, refers to a Hindu ruler, Nerun, who built a fort, or kot, there. Hyderabad continues to be a **strategic** location, though today it is important as a centre for transport and communications rather than for military defence.

Born from the river

The modern city of Hyderabad was founded in 1768 following a gradual change in the course of the Indus. In around 1758 the Indus flooded the capital of the Sindh region, at Khudabad. The ruler of Sindh, Ghulam Shah Kalhora, set out to find a new site for his capital city. He decided on the site that is now Hyderabad, and on the hill built a fort that still stands today.

FACT

With a length of 2 km (1.25 miles), the Shahi Bazaar in Hyderabad is one of the longest in Pakistan.

The modern city of Hyderabad is located close to its ancient hill-top position.

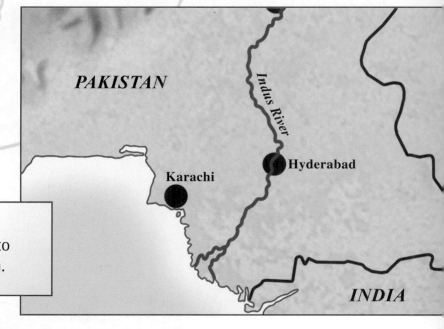

28

The new settlement was named after the prophet Mohammed's son-in-law, Ali, also known as Haidar. In 1782–83 Hyderabad came under the control of the Talpurs, a tribe from western Pakistan. They kept Hyderabad as the capital of Sindh and continued to develop the city.

The Sindh region produced a bounty of food every year, thanks to the annual floodwaters of the Indus. Hyderabad became a busy market town, trading farm produce for manufactured goods such as textiles, household goods and luxury items like jewellery. As a result, Hyderabad became a centre for expert craftspeople, and the central bazaar (market) became one of the most important in Pakistan.

River trade

As the British expanded their Indian colony into modern-day Pakistan they were quick to recognize the benefits of the Indus. As early as 1809 they had begun to deal with the Talpur rulers in Hyderabad to gain passage up the Indus. In 1843 British forces, under Sir Charles Napier, defeated the Talpur army and seized control of Hyderabad. This also gave the British control of the Indus and the Sindh region, and marked the end of an era in Hyderabad. Although the city continued to be of great importance, it lost its title as capital of Sindh, as the British established a new capital in Karachi.

29

The electricity produced by the Kotri barrage helps support local industries.

Commercial centre

The Indus River remains vitally important to the settlement of Hyderabad. It provides transportation to neighbouring settlements and water for **agriculture**, industry and domestic use. The Indus became increasingly important when the Kotri **barrage** was built just upstream of Hyderabad in 1955. This barrage provided **irrigation** water that more than doubled the area that could be farmed around Hyderabad. It also benefited the water-thirsty cotton industry. Pakistan is the world's fourth-largest producer of cotton, producing around 9 per cent of the world total in 2001–02. Hyderabad is in the centre of one of Pakistan's main cotton-producing areas so the city has developed into a major cotton-processing centre.

In turn, its cotton has made Hyderabad an attractive location for the textile industry. The city is close to the raw material (cotton yarn) and has a plentiful supply of water. Textile production uses large quantities of water in the washing, dyeing and bleaching processes, and is often located alongside rivers.

FACT

Cotton first originated in Pakistan. It is now cultivated in 90 countries and is probably the most widely used fabric in the world.

The Kotri barrage also supplies electricity to Hyderabad. The electricity is produced as the Indus passes through generators in the barrage. The combination of electricity and water supplies has attracted several other industries to Hyderabad, including cement, leather, and paper manufacturers.

A cotton factory in Hyderabad. Water from the river is used to process and transport the cotton.

Industries are also attracted to Hyderabad's good transport links. The city provides the main crossing point over the Indus for road and rail traffic travelling between Karachi, to the west, and Islamabad, to the east. These important links have now replaced the river as the main form of transport because they are considered more convenient and offer greater flexibility than the fixed route of the Indus. The construction of barrages across the Indus has also reduced river transportation, as they disrupt the **navigation** of the river.

Labour demand

Many people have moved to Hyderabad in search of work in the city's growing industries. Others have found work providing services for the industrial workers such as shops, banks, restaurants, transport and leisure facilities. As a result the city has grown rapidly over the last fifty years. The city is gradually spreading outwards as new housing is built. Between 1961 and 2000 the population of Hyderabad more than doubled, reaching around 1.2 million people. Pakistan has one of the highest population growth rates in the world, so Hyderabad will continue to expand even if no more people move to the city. By 2015 Hyderabad's population is expected to be around 1.9 million.

Badghirs

Hyderabad's climate is hot for much of the year, but people have developed an ingenious way of cooling down their houses. During the hot summer months a cool breeze blows from the south-west, up the Indus delta towards Hyderabad. In order to benefit from this breeze people have constructed 'badghirs' on their roof tops. These look a little like chimneys but have open slats that allow the cool breeze to enter and pass into the house below.

Environmental pressures

Hyderabad is one of the biggest city to be located on the Indus and it contributes more than many others to the environmental pressures on the river. Large volumes of water are extracted for industry and farming. Waste from farmers' fields, households and industries, such as **tanneries**, textiles and paper-making, is dumped in the Indus. The waste water from industries is often fed back into the Indus without any treatment, though it can contain chemicals and heavy metals. This waste pollutes the river and is dangerous for local wildlife and people using the water further downstream.

The use of chemicals in farming has led to higher levels of water pollution in the Indus River.

Agriculture also causes water pollution. Farmers use chemicals such as **pesticides** and fertilizers to help their crops to grow. Some of these chemicals mix with irrigation or rain water and end up back in the Indus. The chemicals can lower the quality of the river water and kill local plant and animal life. The river water can also become unsafe for humans. If people continue to drink heavily polluted water it can cause serious illnesses and even death.

1768	1782–83	c.1809
Hyderabad is founded as the capital of Sindh by Ghulam Shah Kalhora.	Hyderabad is taken over by the Talpurs from Baluchistan.	British negotiate with Hyderabad Talpurs to use the Indus.

A woman collects water from the Indus. Many people rely on the untreated waters of the Indus to meet their household water needs.

One of the biggest causes of water pollution is the poor treatment of human sewage from settlements along the Indus. Most sewage finds its way back into the river untreated or treated to a very basic level. It can easily **contaminate** drinking water supplies with water-borne diseases. If it is used to irrigate crops it can also contaminate food supplies. Water-borne diseases kill 10 per cent of Pakistani children before they reach the age of one. Overall, polluted water is blamed for around 40 per cent of all deaths in Pakistan. Hyderabad is particularly at risk from water pollution because it receives the pollutants from settlements upstream as well as those generated by the city itself. In 2002 the Sindh Environmental Protection Agency launched a project to monitor water pollution in and around Hyderabad. This is seen as a first step to cleaning up the Indus.

Humans have created environmental pressures along the entire length of the Indus. The **extraction** of water for human use is one of the biggest pressures because it reduces the amount of water in the river. The main impact is felt in the lower **reaches** of the Indus, south of Hyderabad. Besides extraction, land on both sides of the river is being converted either to farmland or housing, as settlements expand. This causes a loss of the river habitat and wildlife that once lived there. Pollution also affects most of the river. These environmental pressures are expected to get worse as the settlements of the Indus grow larger in the future.

1843	1947	1955
British defeat the Talpur army and take control of Hyderabad.	Hyderabad becomes part of newly independent Pakistan.	Kotri barrage is built just upstream of Hyderabad.

Karachi: a mega-city

Humble beginnings

Today Karachi is one of the world's twenty biggest cities, but it started out as a quiet fishing village called Kalachi-jo-Goth. Located at the northern end of the vast Indus **delta,** it was surrounded by a collection of islands amongst the delta's **mangrove swamps.** The area also had a natural harbour bordering the Arabian Sea. It was this that first attracted people to build a settlement at Kalachi-jo-Goth.

The Talpurs gained control of the land around Karachi at the end of the 18th century and built a simple mud fort to protect the harbour and fishing village. The village soon grew into a small town and by 1818 had a population of around 13,000 people. The arrival of the British launched the development of Karachi, with Sir Charles Napier declaring, 'One day she [Karachi] will be the Queen of the East'.

Connection to the world

By 1843 British control had spread to Hyderabad and the entire Sindh region. The British saw that Karachi was important for controlling trade on the Indus, and moved the capital of Sindh from Hyderabad to Karachi. Troops were brought in to protect

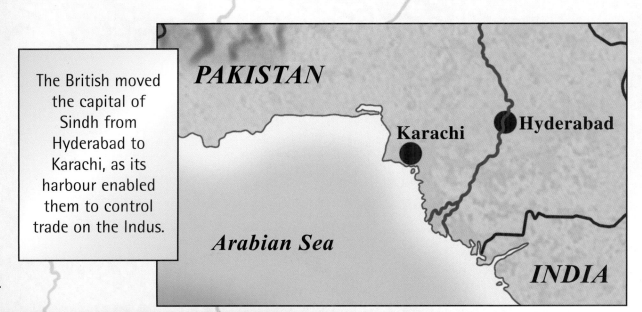

The British moved the capital of Sindh from Hyderabad to Karachi, as its harbour enabled them to control trade on the Indus.

PAKISTAN

Karachi

Hyderabad

Arabian Sea

INDIA

Goods being transported from East Pakistan to West Pakistan through the harbour at Karachi in 1956.

the region, and Karachi grew as traders arrived to provide the army with services and goods. An administrative district was also established to manage not just Karachi, but all of Sindh. The British also developed Karachi's port, allowing the trade of Sindh's agricultural riches to the rest of the world.

The British set up river transport companies such as the Indus Steam Flotilla and the Orient Inland Steam **Navigation** Company. These companies brought farm produce such as wheat down the Indus, through the delta and into Karachi's port. The main crop, cotton, was shipped from Karachi to the textile mills of Great Britain.

River trade on the Indus was soon booming and after just eighteen years of British control the value of goods traded from Karachi had increased sevenfold to £855,103 in 1856. The great wealth to be made in the Indus region attracted several British companies and merchants who set up offices and warehouses in Karachi. In turn Karachi's population grew, as people came to take advantage of new job opportunities. It had reached around 57,000 by 1856.

The boom years

Karachi's development received an unexpected boost from America between 1861–65. The civil war in America severely disrupted the supply of cotton from American plantations to the textile mills of Great Britain. Searching for an alternative source of cotton, British cotton-producers turned to Karachi and the cotton of the Indus. Construction of the Sindh railway in 1861 connected Karachi to the cotton- and wheat-growing areas around Hyderabad and Kotri, and then further into the cotton-growing regions of Punjab to the north when the railway was extended in 1869. This dramatically increased the trade passing through Karachi. As the country's leading sea port, Karachi was further helped by the Suez Canal, which opened in 1869 to connect Europe to Asia. It made Karachi the country's closest port to Great Britain.

Karachi handles an incredible 95 per cent of all Pakistan's foreign trade.

By 1872 the value of trade passing through Karachi had reached £5 million a year, bringing great wealth to the city. Port facilities were modernized to cope with the growth in trade and many of Karachi's finest buildings, often very British in style, were constructed during this period. Empress market, now a thriving fruit and vegetable market, was built to resemble the market halls found in northern England during the mid-19th century, for example.

Still thriving

Karachi has continued to thrive as a city ever since. When Pakistan became independent in 1947, Karachi remained the capital until Islamabad was chosen as its replacement in 1958. Despite losing its status as capital, Karachi has remained the most economically important city in Pakistan, due to its favourable position as the gateway to the Indus valley. Today it handles a wide variety of goods from across Pakistan, though cotton continues to be a major export. The river plays less of a role in the transportation of goods today, which are instead taken by road or rail. The Indus is still vital in Karachi's development, however, as it supports many businesses and industries relied upon for the city's trade. Karachi is also dependent on the Indus as a source of drinking water.

Today, in Pakistan, goods are often transported by road, in lorries, like these, rather than by river.

Rapid growth

Karachi needed a plentiful labour supply to help build the city and run the rapidly growing port. As a result people came from other parts of India, and elsewhere, in their thousands. The city expanded rapidly. With more people came an increased demand for goods and services and so, in turn, more labourers were needed. Others arrived hoping to share in the wealth being made in Karachi and some set up their own businesses. Between 1901 and 1941 Karachi's population grew by 300,000 to reach 436,000. This is the same as just over 20 people arriving in the city every day and never leaving!

This increase in population was set to continue. In 1947 Pakistan and India gained their independence from Britain. They had both been part of one large British colony, but when they became independent they divided to form two new countries. This division was known as the **partition**. Before partition, Karachi had attracted people from all over India. It had a mixed population of about 51 per cent Hindu and 42 per cent Muslim.

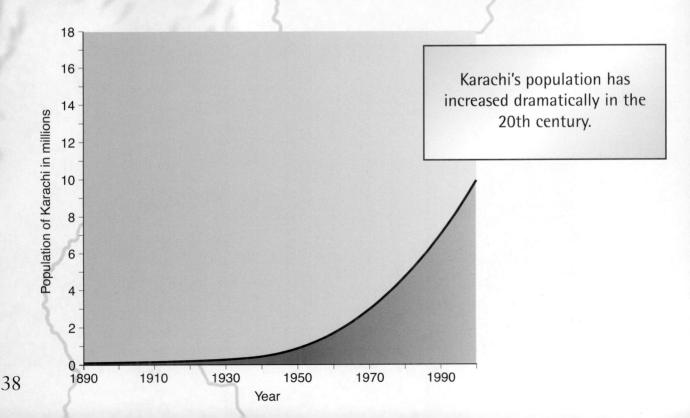

Karachi's population has increased dramatically in the 20th century.

This village in the Indus delta region has been abandoned because salt water intrusion has made the land useless.

During partition a mass migration took place. Hindus moved to the mainly Hindu country of India whilst Muslims from India moved to Pakistan, which was mainly Muslim. Most of Karachi's Hindu population **emigrated** but the city gained at least 600,000 Muslim **immigrants**. The population of Karachi more than doubled in just four years, reaching over a million people by 1951. The mix of Karachi's population also changed to around 94 per cent Muslim and just 2 per cent Hindu. Karachi's population has continued to expand at an incredible rate ever since partition. More and more people arrive in the city on an almost daily basis.

Indus refugees

*Some of the more recent arrivals in Karachi have been people from the Indus delta region. The **extraction** of water further up the Indus has caused the amount of water reaching the Indus delta to fall drastically in recent decades. This is now having a major impact on the delta region and its people. As the Indus waters fall, sea water flows into the delta region to take its place – a process known as salt water intrusion. Sea water is saline (salty) but many of the crops and fish that were once harvested in the delta cannot survive in salt water. It has been estimated that 250,000 hectares of agricultural fields have been lost due to salt water intrusion over the last 50 years. With their livelihoods threatened or lost, many farmers and fishermen have sought refuge with their families in nearby Karachi.*

Population overload?

One of Karachi's biggest problems is that its infrastructure (roads, water supplies, electricity, etc.) has not kept pace with population growth. Around 40 per cent of Karachi's residents live in slum settlements, known as 'katchi abadis', in and around the city. As the city continues to expand, many new arrivals end up in these crowded slums. Others begin to build new slums on any available patch of land. Enormous problems have been caused by Karachi's rapid and unplanned development, such as a lack of schools and hospitals, chaotic and dirty streets, and growing crime. They have led many experts to believe that the city is suffering from population overload.

Water pollution

Water pollution is a big problem in Karachi. Its sewerage system is inefficient and the majority of households are not even connected to it. Vast amounts of sewage are simply dumped into open channels and streams that flow into the Indus delta.

Open sewers run through the slums of Karachi. The sewage flows into the Indus.

c.1775–1800	1818	1839	1856	1861
Talpurs gain control of the land around Karachi.	Karachi develops into a small town.	British gain control of Karachi from the Talpurs.	Karachi becomes a busy port at the mouth of the Indus.	Railway is opened connecting Karachi to Sindh province.

Fishermen sorting palla by size in Karachi. Pollution in the Indus has seriously affected the fishing industry.

Karachi's industries dump much of their waste water in a similar way. Ships visiting the port add to the pollution by dumping waste and spilling oil into the delta.

The Indus delta receives a constant cocktail of raw sewage, toxic chemicals and solid waste. This affects not just the quality of water in the delta but the plants and animals that live there too. Upstream extraction of water means less fresh water reaches the delta. This results in the polluting chemicals building up in the delta region rather than being washed out to sea.

These problems have badly affected the fishing industry. The Indus delta provides about 70 per cent of the coastal fish caught in Pakistan.

As the delta deteriorates so too does the fish catch. The catch of two important fish species, palla and dangri, fell by two-thirds between 1986 and 2001.

Karachi needs to introduce tighter controls on water pollution to better protect the Indus delta if it is to continue growing, or the pollution will increase as the population does. Some scientists warn that the delta **ecosystem** could collapse. This would cause thousands of people to lose their livelihoods and end up in the slums of Karachi.

1861–65	1869	1947	1958	c.1980 onwards
Karachi's cotton exports are boosted by the American Civil War.	Railway is extended from Karachi into Punjab.	Karachi becomes capital of newly independent Pakistan.	Islamabad replaces Karachi as the capital of Pakistan.	Refugees from the Indus delta move to Karachi.

The Indus of tomorrow

Gifts of the Indus

The **settlements** focused on in this book all exist because the Indus River flows through or past them. The Indus is truly a great provider. It brings life to a part of the world that would otherwise be a barren, virtually lifeless desert. Over the 5000 years or so that humans have settled along the river they have learned how to manipulate and manage the river for their own benefit. This has brought great wealth to the region as the remains of Mohenjo-daro, or the grand buildings of Karachi, show.

Developments in technology allowed people to gain even greater control of the river. The Sukkur **barrage**, for example, enabled them to create an **irrigation** scheme on the Indus that remains the largest in the world. Progress in transportation opened up the Indus to new trading opportunities and led to the development of some of its largest cities in Hyderabad and Karachi, which continue to play a major role in world trade today.

Trees for better Environment

PLANTED BY
PTC PAKISTAN TOBACCO COMPANY LIMITED

Attempts are being made, through the planting of mangrove nurseries, like this one, to care for the river environment of the Indus.

These workers are lining an irrigation canal near Sukkur. Lining canals improves their efficiency and will help to reduce pressure on the Indus.

Caring for the Indus

Unfortunately, human activities along the Indus have had a negative affect on the river itself. The Indus' settlements **extract** an increasing amount of water for their rapidly growing populations. They also generate a great deal of waste, which is often untreated. Much of it is dumped back into the Indus, causing pollution and threatening life further downstream. The poor state of the Indus **delta** is a clear sign of the damage being done. Shortages of irrigation water also warn that the Indus is under pressure.

Measures such as reducing industrial pollution or improving the efficiency of the irrigation network would improve the situation. The problem for the Indus settlements, however, is their continuing pace of population growth. In Pakistan the population is expected to more than double to 345 million by 2050. The majority of these people will live in settlements along the Indus and its **tributaries**. This increase in population will make reducing pressure on the river a major challenge. In the past, great civilizations have collapsed because they have failed to take care of the river that provides for them. The people of the Indus valley have lived with the river for thousands of years. In the future they must learn to protect the great Indus River, so that generations to come can benefit from its waters.

Timeline

c.3300 BC	Small villages are established in the area around Mohenjo-daro.
c.2600	Building of planned city begins at Mohenjo-daro.
c.2600–1800	Mohenjo-daro is a thriving trade city.
c.1800	Mohenjo-daro falls into decline and is later abandoned.
AD 900	First **settlements** are established in the area around Leh.
962	Sukkur is founded.
c.1250	Sukkur is established as a busy port.
c.1550	Leh is founded as the new capital of Ladakh.
1768	Hyderabad is founded as Sindh's capital.
1782–83	Hyderabad is taken over by the Talpurs from Baluchistan.
c.1809	British negotiate with Hyderabad Talpurs to use the Indus.
1818	Karachi develops into a small town.
1834	Zorawar Singh captures Leh for the Maharaja of Kashmir.
1839	British gain control of Karachi from the Talpurs.
c.1840s	Leh becomes part of British-controlled India.
c.1842	British gain control of Sukkur.
1843	British defeat the Talpur army and take control of Hyderabad.
1847	First plans are made for a **barrage** at Sukkur.
1856	Karachi becomes a busy port at the mouth of the Indus.
1861	Railway is opened connecting Karachi to Sindh province.
1861–65	Karachi's cotton exports are boosted by the American Civil War.
1869	Railway is extended from Karachi into Punjab.
1888	Lansdowne Rail Bridge is built across the Indus at Sukkur.
1922	Ruins of Mohenjo-daro are discovered.
1923	Construction of Sukkur barrage begins.
1932	Sukkur barrage is opened.
1947	Sukkur, Hyderabad and Karachi become part of newly independent Pakistan. Leh becomes part of independent India.
1948	First attempts are made to conserve Mohenjo-daro.
1955	Kotri barrage is built just upstream of Hyderabad.
1958	Islamabad is chosen to replace Karachi as capital of Pakistan.
1980	Mohenjo-daro becomes a **World Heritage Site**.
c.1980	Refugees from the Indus **delta** move to Karachi.
1984	Ladakh Ecological Development Group is established to protect Leh.

Further resources

Books

Country Profiles: Pakistan,
Khawar Mumtaz et al. (Oxfam, 2003)

Excavating the Past: Indus,
Ilona Aronovsky and Sujata Gopinath (Heinemann Library, 2004)

Nations of the World: India,
Anita Dalal (Raintree, 2003)

Understanding People in the Past: The Indus valley,
Naida Kirkpatrick (Heinemann Library (US), 2002)

Websites

British Museum (www.ancientindia.co.uk)
A site designed to support the national curriculum that focuses
on Ancient India. It has a section on the Indus valley that
includes an **archaeologist's** note pad and interactive maps
to explore the digs at Mohenjo-daro.

**Ecotopics International News Service
(www.ecotopics.com/articles/indus-at-risk.htm)**
A page with an interesting article about the problems of salt
water and over-**extraction** in the Indus valley. It considers the
future of the Indus delta.

Indus Civilization Guide (www.moenjodaro.org)
An online guide to the Indus **civilization** that focuses on the site
of Mohenjo-daro. Includes images of the ruins and what the city
may have looked like in the past.

Glossary

agriculture practice of growing crops or raising animals for food or to sell

altitude distance (or height) above sea level, measured in feet or metres

archaeologist someone who specializes in investigating the past from evidence that was left behind, which usually lies buried under ground

barrage artificial barrier that is normally built across a river to provide protection against floods or to produce hydro-electricity

British Empire period in which Britain had political and military control over large parts of the world. At its greatest between the early 17th and late 19th centuries.

Buddhism form of religion, particularly common in central Asia (Tibet and northern India)

citadel fortified building in or near a city, often where rulers lived for protection

civilization an organized society

contaminate to make something become unclean. For example, water can be contaminated when it becomes polluted.

cultivated land that is farmed

delta area at the mouth of a river formed by the deposit of sand and soil in a triangular shape

ecosystem environment such as a pond, river or forest, and all the animals and plants that live within it

emigrate leave a place (normally a country) to live elsewhere

excavate dig up or unearth something

extraction to remove by force. Often used to describe the taking of water from a river.

fertilizers chemicals that are applied to crops to feed them and encourage growth

gorge natural cutting through a landscape formed by a river

immigrant person who arrives in a place (normally a country) from elsewhere

irrigation watering crops using specially created systems. Normally used in areas of low rainfall.

mangrove swamp form of forest that grows in shallow water around rivers or coastal areas in tropical countries

melt-water water that has melted from glaciers or ice-fields in mountainous areas

milling conversion of raw material (such as wheat) into finished goods (such as flour)

navigation act of directing or moving a boat along a river or across a lake or sea

nutrients substances that provide food to plants or animals. Soils, for example, carry mineral nutrients that help plants to grow.

partition process by which Britain's Indian colony was divided into India and Pakistan at independence in 1947

pesticides chemicals used in farming to kill pests that can otherwise damage crops

pictorial using pictures instead of letters or words as a form of communication

plain wide, normally level area of land often found to either side of a river in its middle and lower reaches

plateau level top of a hill or mountain

reaches part of a river's course. Rivers are normally divided into upper, middle and lower reaches.

ritual ceremonial or traditional practice performed by people. Often associated with a religion, but can also be linked to specific cultures.

sediment soil-like material that is carried in water

settlement place that has people living in it permanently. Settlements can vary in size from a small village to a large city.

strategic vital part of a plan (strategy). For example a bridge may be a strategic target in a military campaign.

tannery the name given to a place where animal skins are tanned as part of the leather-making process

trading post store or town (often in a remote location) where local produce is exchanged or sold for goods and supplies from elsewhere

tributary river or stream that joins another, normally larger, river

uncultivated land that has not been farmed

water table level under the ground below which the earth or rocks are filled with water. A water table can rise or fall over time.

World Heritage Site site of cultural or natural importance. In 2003 there were 754 World Heritage Sites.

Index